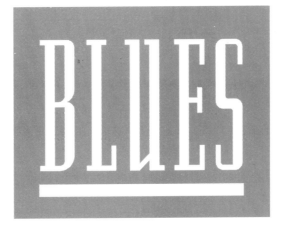

by ROBBEN FORD

GW00771718

The philosophy of the *REH HOTLINE SERIES* is to give a larger and varied vocabulary of licks and melodic ideas. Many guitarists want to have their own original style and feel they shouldn't copy licks from other players. In reality, it is a proven fact by most top *original* players that it is very beneficial, if not necessary, to study the music of other guitarists. With the *Hotline* books you will soon hear and understand melodies and how they relate to chords. *Hotlines* are also great for building chops and will give you an arsenal of ideas to fall back on. In addition, you will develop an understanding of improvising theory by learning and analyzing the lines which are built from scales, arpeggios and intervals.

Here are some suggestions to help you get the most out of *Hotlines:*

▼ *Play them in all keys and, if possible, in different octaves.*

▼ *Since many of the lines are written in simple 16th notes for quick learning, experiment by breaking them up rhythmically (syncopating) or phrasing them in different parts of the bar.*

▼ *Feel free to add effects like hammer-ons, pull-offs, slurs and bends.*

▼ *Experiment with the lines over different chords from the ones suggested.*

▼ *Although the author's fingerings and positions are shown for each of the Hotlines, you may want to experiment with your own fingerings.*

▼ *The last and most important thing is to work the lines (in whole or in part) into your playing right away.*

Copyright © 1984, 1994 by HAL LEONARD CORPORATION
International Copyright Secured   All Rights Reserved

For all works contained herein:
Unauthorized copying, arranging, adapting, recording or public performance is an infringement of copyright.
Infringers are liable under the law.

HAL•LEONARD™
CORPORATION

7777 W. BLUEMOUND RD. P.O. BOX 13819 MILWAUKEE, WI 53213

The first 48 bars (Hotlines 1-19) though broken up into lines of 2, 3 and 4 bars, are actually a series of four 12 bar Blues progressions and can be played that way. The idea is to give you some sense of flow, and also help learn the form of 12 bar Blues.

HOTLINE # 1

The opening line here is a classic blues line. Observe the jump from the first Bb eighth note on the E string to the second one on the B string. Subtle changes like this are very important in Blues playing.

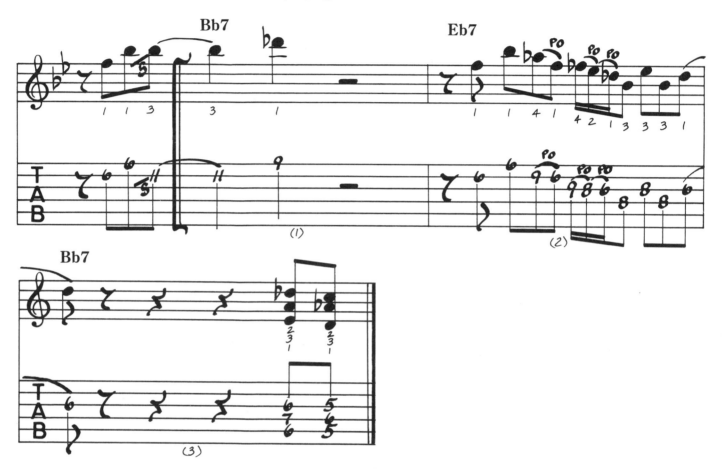

HOTLINE # 2

The first 2 eighth notes here are played first by pulling the G string from an Eb note to an F note, then hitting the 2nd eighth on the B string, similar to Hotline #1. The 2 notes in the 2nd bar are the 5th and 3rd of the IV chord (Eb7) of the Blues progression, spelling, or sounding out the key change.

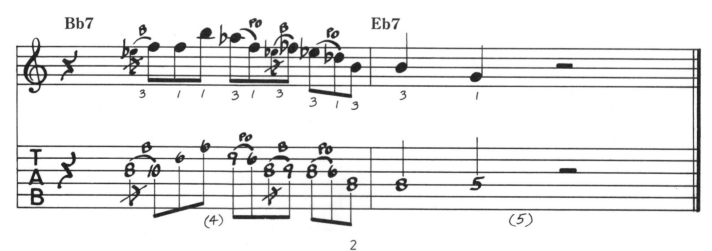

HOTLINE # 3

The first note here (high F) should sound drawn out, like you are really pulling on it. This is a subtle phrasing technique which I hope you can hear on the tape. The point is to exaggerate the bend a little.

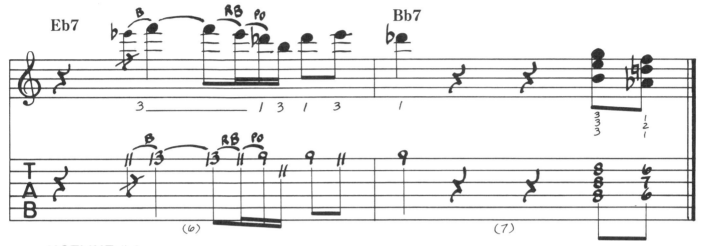

HOTLINE # 4

In this line again the Bb eighth notes in the 1st bar are played first on the E string and then on the B string, creating a certain tension. The phrase in the 2nd bar plays right off the V chord (F7) spelling out the chord for the listener.

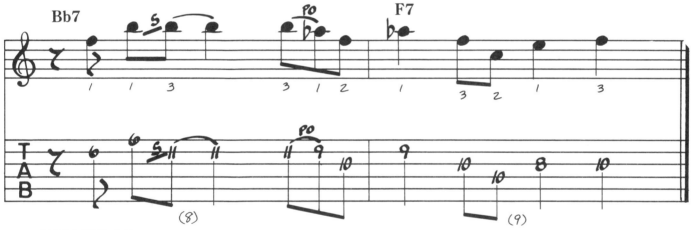

HOTLINE # 5

This is the first line that introduces something predominant in my playing, which is the deliberate use of the minor 3rd (Db) and major 6th (G) juxtaposed against each other. Ordinarily the dominant 7th (G#) would probably be used. This sound creates a certain texture I've always liked.

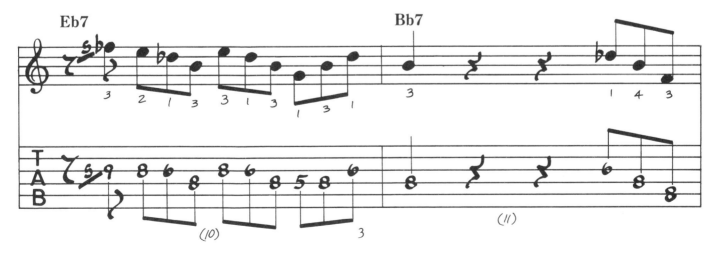

HOTLINE # 5   (cont.)

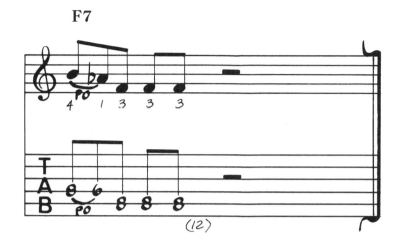

HOTLINE # 6

This is something Texas blues guitarist Albert Collins might play, and it should be played with real punch. Experiment and try playing it with just your fingers.

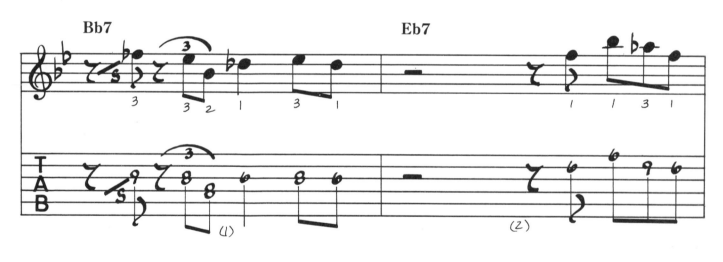

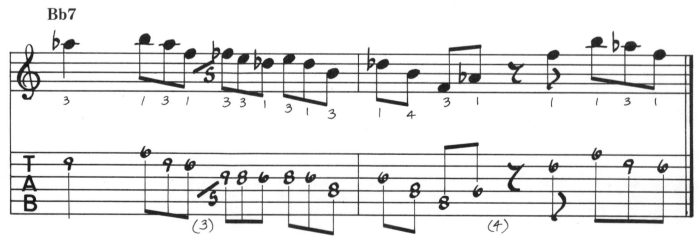

HOTLINE # 7

Put a lot of 'grease' on the slide from the Ab note to the Bb. The quarter note triplet should sound exaggerated and drawn out here.

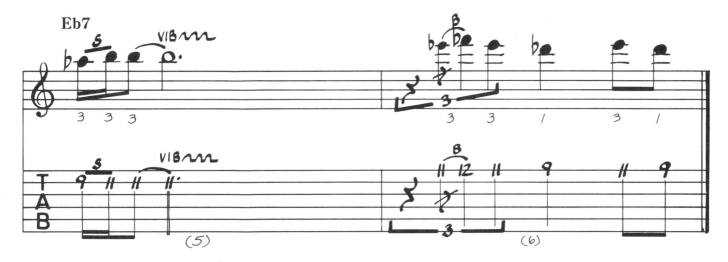

HOTLINE # 8

The slide from the Fb (E) grace note to the Eb should be played real punchy. The slide up to the second Bb eighth note in bar two occurs here again.

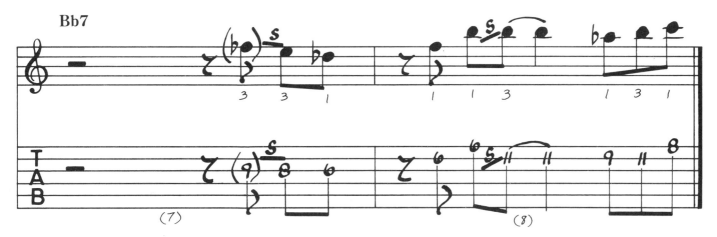

HOTLINE # 9

This line incorporates the use of "Theme Development" taking the phrase in bar one and developing it both rhythmically and tonally in bar two, stretching it out a bit.

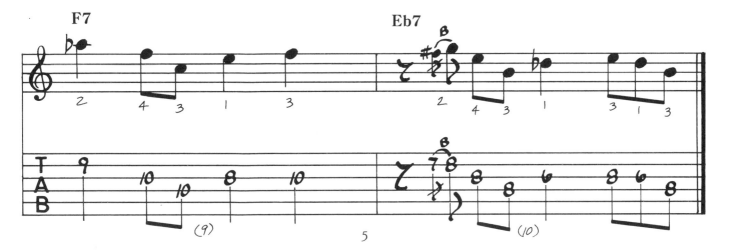

HOTLINE #10

The first 2 triplets in bar one are interesting. The same leap occurs from the first
Bb eighth note on the E string to the second Bb eighth on the B string, and the eighth
note rest between them creates a gap, almost like a deliberate stumble. Once again
a certain tension is created. The quick 16th notes in bar 2 create a little break from
the basic triplet feel that's been pretty constant so far.

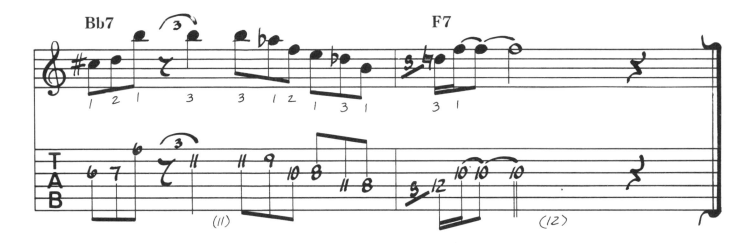

HOTLINE #11

This line uses Theme Development again, taking the phrase in the first bar and
stretching it out (quite a bit this time) in bars three and four.

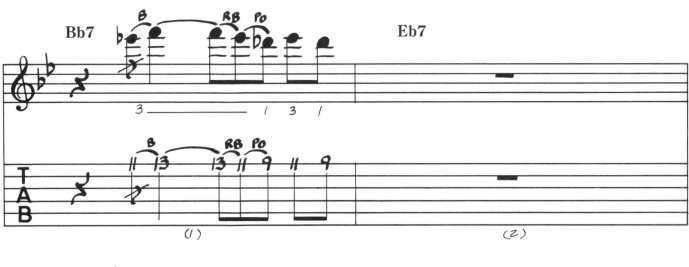

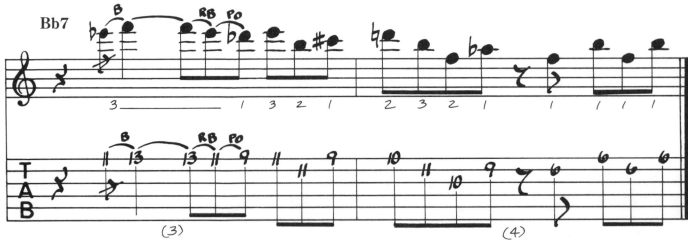

6

HOTLINE #12

Note the Hammer-On in bar one. The double stop (using 2 notes at once) in bar 2 puts the minor 3rd and major 6th flat against each other creating that sound and tension I mentioned earlier in the book.

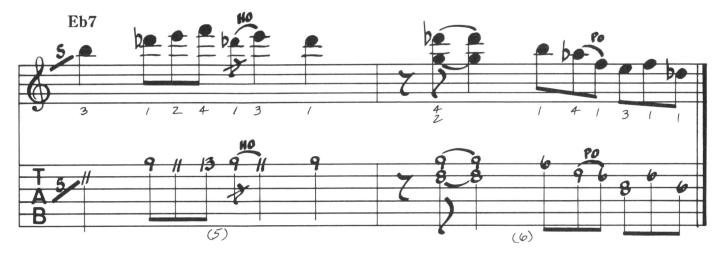

HOTLINE #13

The valuable part of this line is the position it's played in on the guitar neck. It is like playing in the relative minor key (Gm7 in this case), which is a good position for playing major Pentatonic lines in the tonic key (Bb in this case).

HOTLINE #14

This is a four bar line, and a lot of the notes sort of jump around. The phrasing has the quality of stopping and starting, sort of a stumbling effect.

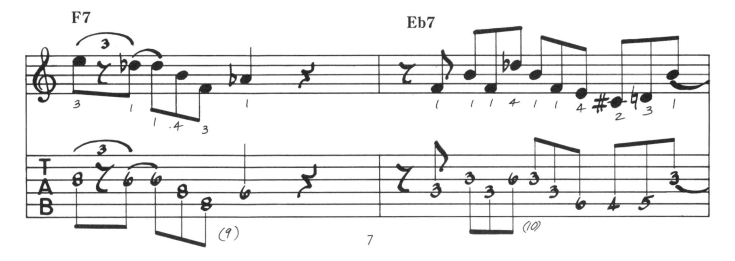

HOTLINE #14   (cont.)

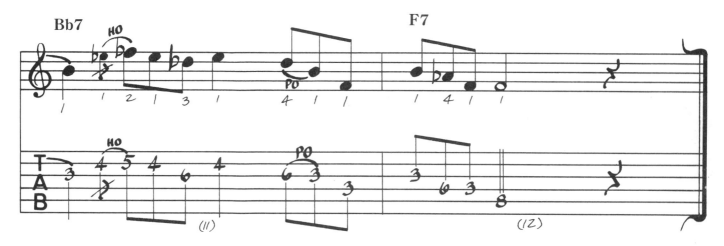

HOTLINE #15

Double stops are used in this line a lot. The first bar I find to be very funky. It should be played with the fingers rather than the pick. I use my first and second fingers on the B and E strings and my thumb on the G string.

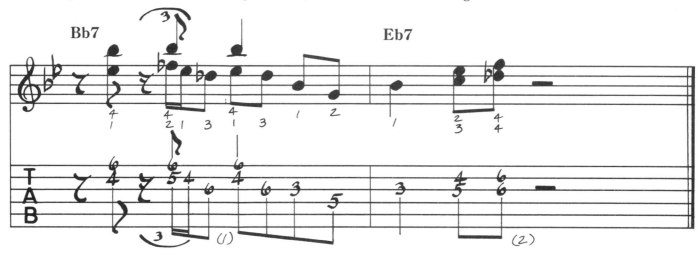

HOTLINE #16

This line should be played with the fingers also (except for the last half of bar 2). The 2nd and 3rd fingers play the notes on the G and B strings, and the thumb plays the notes on the D string.

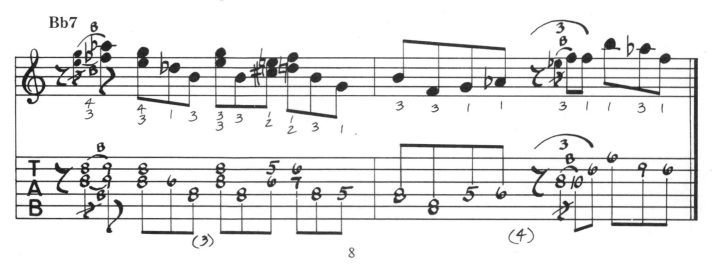

HOTLINE #17

The 2nd bar of this line should be played with a slight crescendo of feeling (more so than volume).

HOTLINE #18

Here again is the use of the minor 3rd and major 6th color. Also, the way the notes jump around in almost randon fashion creates a certain tension.

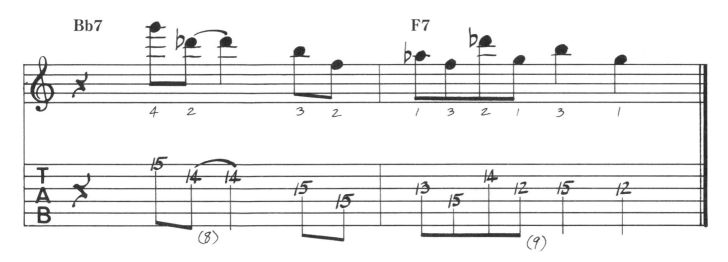

HOTLINE #19

The phrasing in this line should be very punchy as in the Texas blues style playing like Albert Collins.

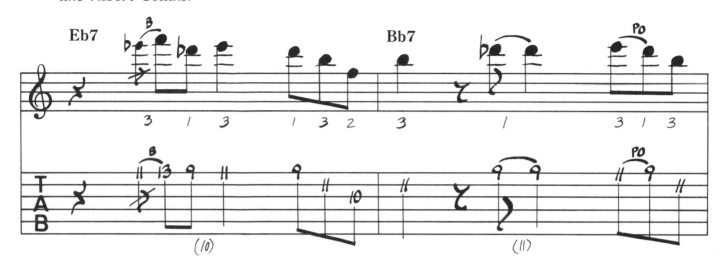

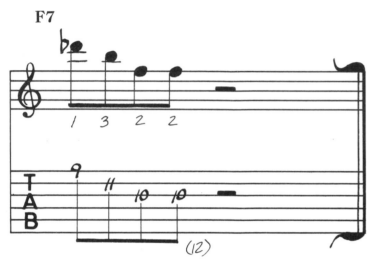

This ends the 12 bar Blues section.

HOTLINE #20

The first bar here is virtually a G7add9 arpeggio. Bar two uses a bend on the G string from C to D and then plays the 2nd D on the B string which is a classic blues style of playing.

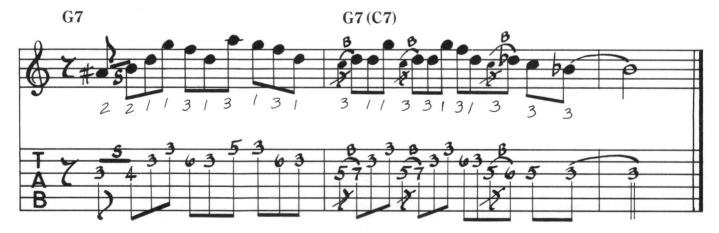

HOTLINE #21

This line could be the opening line for a slow blues, but sounds good at an up tempo shuffle feel as well.

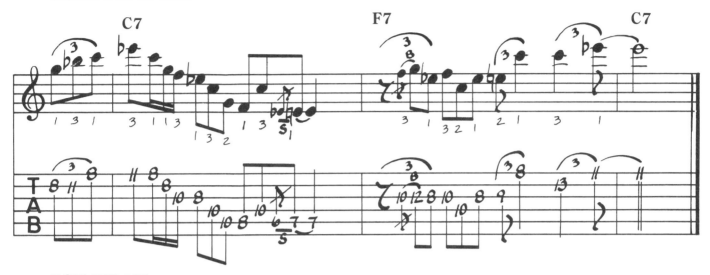

HOTLINE #22

This line sounds best when played as the last two bars of a slow blues progression.

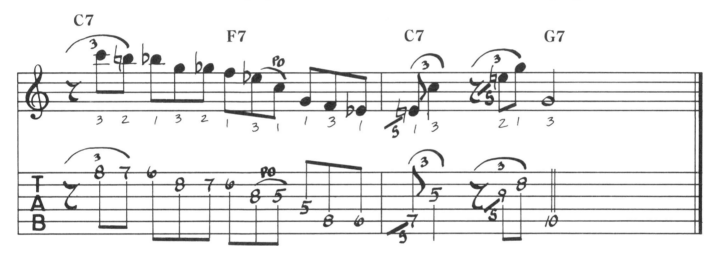

HOTLINE #23

This line could be played in either the 3rd and 4th, or 6th and 7th bars of a blues progression. The 16th note triplet in the 2nd half of bar one sounds different than written, so check the phrasing with the tape.

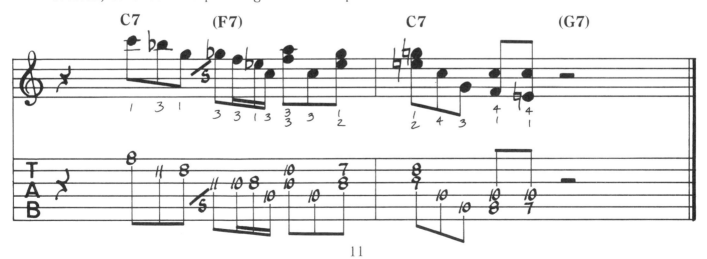

11

HOTLINE #24

Again, here is the use of minor 3rd and major 6th tension. This line could be considered incomplete in that it shouldn't end on the C quarter note, but keep going. Maybe you could add to this line.

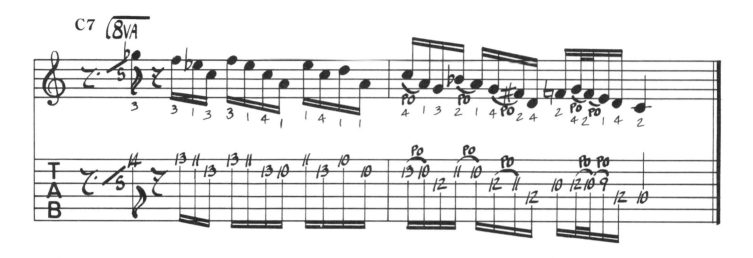

HOTLINE #25

This line works well as an opening 4 bars to a shuffle. The phrasing is tricky here in the first 16th note triplet, and sounds best when played with the fingers.

HOTLINE #26

This could be the opening 4 bars of a 12 bar blues. Watch the 16th note triplet in the 1st bar. This lick sounds best at a shuffle tempo.

HOTLINE #27

This line works well played in the 3rd and 4th bars of a shuffle blues. The notes in the 1st bar basically outline a C major arpeggio and bar 2 starts with the same arpeggio down an octave. Thats the stuff that gives your playing form.

HOTLINE #28

This is more of a 'Jazz' line. It begins by using 4th intervals in the 1st bar. The first 4 eighth notes of bar 2 basically spell a D chord (bending the F note allows it to be major or minor, or both).

Dm7 (D7#9)

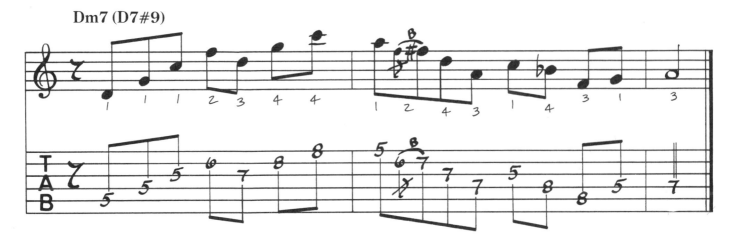

HOTLINE #29

This line is based on a pattern using the A minor Pentatonic scale. The pattern is established with the first 4 notes after the pick-up, and descends in triadic intervals.

Am7

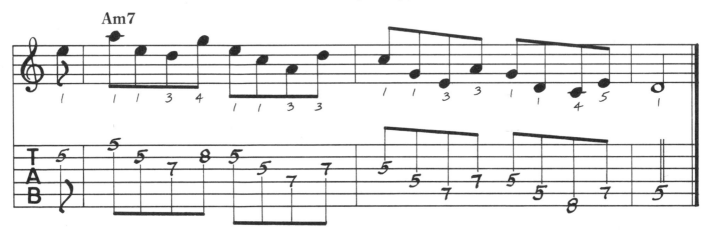

HOTLINE #30

This line basically just runs the C major scale (G Mixolydian mode) and is good in a static chord situation, or could resolve at the end of the 4 bars to a C7 chord.

G7

14

HOTLINE #30 (cont.)

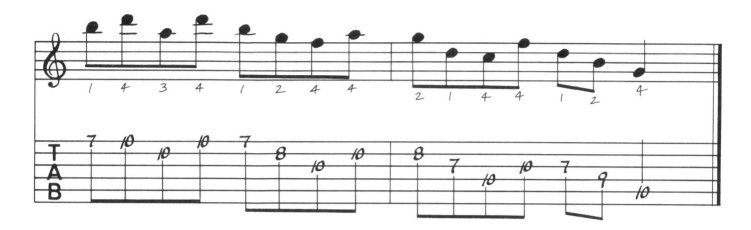

HOTLINE #31

This line is based on a Diminished scale and is a II V I chord change series. There is a diminished scale 4th pattern set up in the 2nd half of the 1st bar which continues through the 2nd bar.

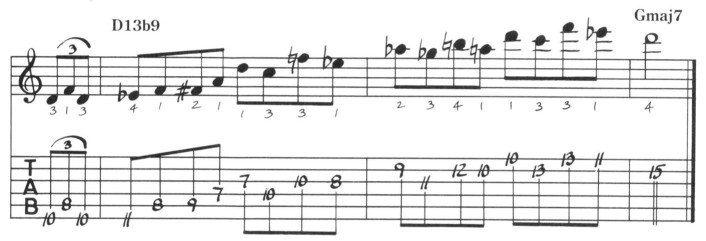

HOTLINE #32

This line is based on the same Diminished scale as #31 but in a different key, and is also a II V progression. The diminished scale is almost always resolving to the tonic note or chord. The scale is a series of half steps and whole steps: G Ab Bb Cb Db D E F G = Ab diminished (G7b9) resolving to C.

HOTLINE #33

This line is based on the use of an Fmaj7 arpeggio against a G7 tonality (once again, the G Mixolydian mode or C scale). A 4 note pattern is set up in the last half of the 3rd bar continuing to the lines end.

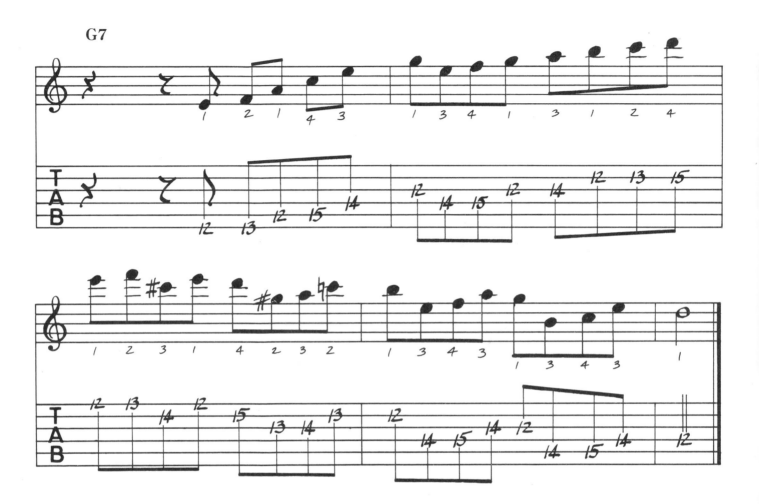

HOTLINE #34

This is a standard II V I chord progression. The scale is similar to the diminished scale presented earlier, but this one is half Diminished and half Whole Tone (Ab Melodic minor = G Ab Bb Cb Db Eb F G).

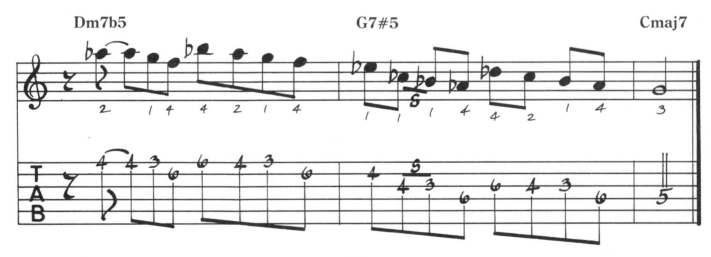